CU00689199

Research & survey in nature conservation

No. 25

**Moorland management:
a literature review**

by

M A Mowforth and C Sydes

Further copies can be obtained from
Publicity Services Branch
Nature Conservancy Council, Northminster House
Peterborough PE1 1UA

ABSTRACT

Moorland dominated by heather <u>Calluna</u> <u>vulgaris</u> is one of the most important components of the British uplands for nature conservation. Much moorland has been lost through land-use changes such as afforestation and pasture improvement. However, current grazing management has also led to loss of heather from parts of many uplands. This report reviews research on grazing and burning to identify the management appropriate to maintain heather and indicates where further research is needed to define good moorland management for wildlife conservation.

CONTENTS

INTRODUCTION AND MANAGEMENT HISTORY

This report reviews the literature relevant to the conservation management of moorland dominated by heather Calluna vulgaris in the British uplands. Heather moorland is found only in the oceanic regions of Europe and forms a unique ecosystem of international significance (Ratcliffe & Thompson 1988). Approximately six million hectares of upland Britain above the upper limit of enclosure are covered by semi-natural vegetation, the major constituent of which is heather-dominated heathland and blanket bog (Bunce & Barr 1988).

Over the past 30-40 years about one million hectares of upland vegetation have been lost to afforestation (Nature Conservancy Council 1984, 1986) and a further 0.25 million hectares has been lost by mechanical cultivation to give agriculturally improved pasture (Parry, Bruce & Harkness 1981; Royal Society for the Protection of Birds 1984). Even where the vegetation has not been modified in these radical ways, species composition can be changed by present management. This is most obvious in the steady replacement of dwarf shrubs, such as heather, by graminoids - the grasses and related plants. The meristems of graminoids are at ground level and therefore are less likely to be destroyed when the plant is grazed or burned, at least by a quickly moving fire (Welch 1984b). The active meristems of woody plants are at the tips of shoots and so are destroyed when shoots are consumed. The upland vegetation of a large part of the Peak District was mapped in 1913; 36% of the vegetation then dominated by heather is now dominated by graminoids (Anderson & Yalden 1981). Analysis of samples of aerial photographs indicates that in Cumbria since the 1940s 70% (297,000 ha) of heather-dominated vegetation has been replaced by unimproved vegetation dominated by graminoids (Nature Conservancy Council 1987).

The loss of woody dwarf shrub heath should concern the grazier as well as the conservationist. Admittedly, heather is much less palatable than grasses to domestic herbivores in spring and early summer but it is evergreen and is one of the few sources of food in winter on the hills. The graminoids that succeed dwarf shrubs are often comparatively unpalatable or deciduous and so not available in winter (Braid & Tervet 1937; Ball et al. 1981). Nardus stricta is the main species to gain dominance in drier habitats, while in wetter habitats Molinia caerulea, Eriophorum vaginatum, Trichophorum cespitosum and Juncus squarrosus increase. The tussocky growth form of some of these species adds to their resistance to grazing. Although palatable grassland dominated by Agrostis and Festuca may replace heather, it is commonly assumed that this may be invaded subsequently by less nutritious species, such as Nardus stricta, if intense grazing continues.

Most moorland occurs below the theoretical tree-line and was once wooded. The dominance of dwarf shrubs is mainly a consequence of felling, burning and grazing. Although they possess apical meristems like trees, dwarf shrubs such as heather have a greater ability to regenerate from the base of a cut or burnt stem and are evidently better able to sustain repeated damage. The studies of pollen and carbon particles preserved in peat and sediments document the decline of woodland and the increasing dominance of dwarf shrubs over the past 2,000 years or so (Birks 1988). It follows that most moorland must be managed by grazing and burning to conserve it from the return of woodland. Only communities on deep peat (blanket bogs) are unlikely to be invaded by trees.

Such evidence as we have suggests that upland vegetation has been managed with increasing intensity in recent decades and centuries. The uplands have been widely grazed and burned since Neolithic times (e.g. Tinsley 1975). Evidence of Norse pastoralists (Welch 1974) and well organised grazing farms belonging to monastic orders in Mediaeval times (Williams 1983) indicates a continuity of management to match the decline of woodland and increasing abundance of dwarf shrubs in the pollen record.

Documentary records indicate that before the 18th century the uplands were exploited by mixed populations of domestic herbivores in summer only; the animals and their owners wisely retreated to their main settlements at lower altitudes in winter. The number of beasts must have been limited by the shortage of winter feed and also by the modest demands of a largely subsistence economy. A trading economy had begun in the Welsh hills by the 15th century, with export of store cattle to the lowlands. This trend spread to all parts of the uplands, but the impact of the cattle on native vegetation was probably relatively limited in extent.

The present system of sheep-farming swept away the traditional management of summer grazing by introducing hardier breeds of sheep able to over-winter in the hills. This process is most notoriously associated with the Scottish Highlands, where the clearances occurred in the late 18th century, but it had happened earlier elsewhere. Where losses of heather to grassland occur today, it is likely to be the intensity of management that is leading to losses - sometimes too much burning and grazing and sometimes too little. Sheep management in the uplands is almost certainly still intensifying; since 1950 the number of sheep recorded by the annual agricultural census from upland parishes in England and Wales has nearly doubled (Royal Society for the Protection of Birds 1984). Although pasture improvement within these parishes must help to support these sheep, many of these pastures are closed for part of the summer to provide grass for winter feed and then animals are displaced to the decreasing area of unimproved moorland.

Sporting use started to have a significant impact on management practices in the uplands during the 19th century. Many estates began to be managed primarily for the red deer Cervus elaphus and the red grouse Lagopus lagopus scoticus. Red deer are an important quarry mainly in the Scottish Highlands (although two herds are also maintained in the Lake District and red deer are hunted on Exmoor). Densities of red deer are generally much lower than those of sheep, but numbers have increased considerably in many parts of the Highlands since 1960 (Stewart 1985). Deer ranching, with much higher densities of animals in paddocks, would have a considerable impact on dwarf shrubs if it were to become extensive (Grant, Bolton & Torvell 1981).

One of the main consequences of management to maximise populations of red grouse has been better control of the extent and frequency of burning which previously, under the control of graziers, was probably haphazard in timing and uncontrolled in extent. Burning improves the nutritional quality of heather and other moorland plants which become increasingly indigestible with age (Gimingham 1972; Kay & Staines 1981). However, burning is still not always used to the benefit of dwarf shrubs in moorland. It is commonly felt that unproductive moors (especially in north-west Scotland) have been burned too frequently, leading to widespread loss of dwarf shrubs. In other areas burning has largely ceased, resulting in stands of old heather which are unlikely to regenerate in the face of intense grazing and are susceptible to tree regeneration where grazing has also ceased. The increased cost of manpower has reduced the availability of skilled labour for burning heather on estates and decreasing numbers of grouse make the process even less economic. This can cause landholders to cease burning, to apply less strict rotations, or to resume uncontrolled, extensive fires for grazing objectives alone.

The NCC must maintain those areas of moorland it has identified as important for wildlife conservation. Problems with present grazing or burning practice are clearly indicated where there is evidence of a decreasing area of heather-dominated moorland, where heather has been recently killed by intensive winter grazing, where burning management has been neglected and the heather is now old, or where recently burned heather shows no, or heavily grazed, regeneration. But what is the correct grazing and burning management that should be recommended? The sections which follow review the published information on burning and grazing effects on heather moorland.

BURNING

Man has affected upland vegetation by fire for a long time, perhaps since the Mesolithic period. Undoubtedly burning contributed to the decline of woodland and the maintenance of heaths and grasslands that replaced the trees. However, the careful, well-controlled burning of moorland vegetation has probably only been practised since the 19th century, when many upland estates became geared to the production of large stocks of red grouse for shooting. Before that time the burning practised by graziers was probably haphazard and the fire, once lit, was uncontrolled (Lovat 1911).

Burning releases nutrients that are held in dead wood and litter. Some of the nutrients, such as nitrogen, are lost as smoke, but the losses may be adequately replenished by rainfall and dust inputs (Hobbs & Gimingham 1987). The exact nutrient budget is still not clear but certainly the nutritional content of plant growth after fire is increased (Gimingham 1972), presumably owing to the increased availability of nutrients, and there is vigorous plant growth (Grant 1968). Therefore regularly burning moorland increases its carrying capacity for herbivores such as sheep and red deer (Gimingham 1972) and helps to maintain good stocks of grouse (Picozzi 1968; Miller, Watson & Jenkins 1970). By removing highly combustible material (Miller, Miles & Heal 1984), it reduces the risk of severe accidental fires which can destroy large areas of moorland in dry summer weather (Radley 1965; Maltby 1980).

Heather may be lost if moorland is burned too frequently or too rarely. Frequent burning will prevent successful regeneration of heather to the advantage of co-dominants such as <u>Molinia</u> <u>caerulea</u>, particularly where the productivity of the vegetation is low (Grant & Milne 1981). In severe cases bare ground may become widespread, decreasing the food available to herbivores and increasing the risk of soil erosion.

Where burning management has been infrequent or has ceased, vegetative regeneration from the old heather bushes may be unsuccessful. Old heather burns hotter and longer than younger heather. A temperature of 940 ^{o}C was recorded in 35-year-old heather but only 500 ^{o}C in 10-year-old heather (Kenworthy 1963). Higher temperatures increase the loss of nitrogen in smoke (Allen 1964; Kenworthy 1964) and reduce vegetative and seedling regeneration (Gimingham 1972). Stands of older heather take at least five years to regain 50% cover while younger heather regains 50% cover in about three years (Grant 1968).

Stands of old heather bushes contain very large amounts of combustible woody tissue and are liable to catch fire accidentally. Such fires are most likely in dry spring or summer weather and pose a direct threat to breeding animals because of this. They may be very extensive and the habitat loss considerable. The substrate can burn for weeks or months and in dry periods even the organic components of the soil can be burnt away to expose bare mineral material (Radley 1965; Maltby 1980). Recolonisation is very slow (Radley 1965).

The optimum burning regime will allow sufficient time for heather to regain dominance but prevent it from accumulating much woody material. Heather should be burned at the late building/early mature phase. Recommended burning regimes for drier heather moorlands are from 6-10 years on Exmoor in southern England (Miller, Miles & Heal 1984) to 10-12 years in Aberdeenshire in north-east Scotland (Gimingham 1972), the difference reflecting potential productivity and climate. A 10-year burning cycle will eventually eliminate heather on blanket bog, where productivity is reduced by the impoverished substrate (Hobbs 1984). Hobbs, working at Moor House NNR in the north of England, records that _Eriophorum vaginatum_ comes to dominate under a 10-year cycle. Heather restoration may take between 11-17 years after burning on blanket bog (Rawes & Hobbs 1979) and heather only regains its full dominance after 20 years (Taylor & Marks 1970; Hobbs 1984). A 20-year burning regime is the recommended minimum to maintain heather on blanket bog. A practical way to adjust the burning regime to take account of local productivity is to burn when the heather is 20-30 cm tall (Grant & Milne 1981; Miller, Miles & Heal 1984), and this could be a suitable basis even for a legal management agreement.

Heather on blanket bog does not exhibit the cycle that has been identified on dry heather moorland and burning may not be required to provide rejuvenation of the bushes (McVean & Lockie 1969; Gimingham 1971; Rawes & Hobbs 1979; Hobbs 1984). Heather stems buried by the growth of _Sphagnum_ and other pleurocarpous mosses produce adventitious roots and these continue the growth of the heather stem, so that stems above the moss layer are comparatively young (Forrest 1971; Hobbs 1984; Hobbs & Gimingham 1987). It has also been argued that burning here does not lead to an increase in grouse numbers (Hobbs 1984) or grazing potential (Rawes & Williams 1973), although it has been demonstrated experimentally in the west of Eire that burning heather on blanket bog can give an increase in lamb production (Lance & Triggs 1974; Lance 1983). Unburnt bog may have greater species diversity than burned bog (Hobbs 1984) and some plants, notably _Sphagnum_ species, appear to be eliminated by burning. Unfortunately, although the substrate is generally waterlogged, extensive stands of unburned neglected woody heather on blanket bogs are subject to accidental fires in dry periods and so firebreaks at least are essential unless considerable losses are acceptable. Neglected blanket bog may also affect the distribution and impact of herbivores on other parts of the moorland grazing unit (see p. 16).

Moorland burning (also called muirburn or swaling) is legally restricted to the period between 1 November and 31 March (15 April in the uplands) in England and Wales by the Heather and Grass Burning (England & Wales) Regulations 1985 and between 1 October and 15 April in Scotland by the Hill Farming Act 1946, which has recently been amended by the Hill Farming Act 1985. Burning moorland vegetation in summer was already illegal in 1607, for Rackham (1986) cites a statute forbidding "raysinge of fires in Moorische Grounds and mountainous Countries" in the north of England between May and September on pain of a month's imprisonment. In Scotland, legal restrictions since 1772 are recorded in the Game (Scotland) Act 1926.

Extensions are possible to allow burning until 15 May if the moor lies above 457 m. Special licences can extend the legal muirburn period to allow burning after unsuitable spring weather and summer burning of heather infested by heather beetle _Lochmaea suturalis_. It is argued that winter burning does not exterminate the heather beetle, as the adults overwinter buried in _Sphagnum_ and damp litter under the plants from the onset of winter until April (Jenkins 1971). In fact infestations are noticeably restricted to neglected heather, so burning at any time will limit the problem. An infestation of the beetle may not necessarily be regarded as a conservation problem, as the loss of heather is likely to be very local.

Moors are usually burnt in the spring (Lovat 1911; Miller 1966; Grant 1968). However, Miller & Miles (1970) and Grant & Milne (1981) suggest that heather regenerates more successfully after autumn fires. Autumn muirburn may also discourage Eriophorum and Trichophorum. These species increase their dominance at the expense of heather after fires. They are probably not affected by spring muirburn, as their buds are dormant until April (Rawes & Hobbs 1979).

Limited grazing decreases, but does not usually prevent, heather regeneration after fire (Lance 1983). It may promote heather cover and dominance by encouraging lateral spread of the bushes. But excessive grazing after burning leads to an increase in bare ground (Rawes & Hobbs 1979). It has been suggested (Grant & Hunter 1968; Grant et al. 1978; Newbould 1979) that a suitable density of sheep may maintain heather in a physiologically young state and reduce the need for burning, as long as consumption remains less than production. Burning is only necessary where grazing under-utilises heather production (Grant & Milne 1981). However the experiments that led to such a conclusion (Grant 1971a) involved sheep feeding on heather in paddocks. Results from these experimental regimes of restricted grazing may not be applicable to extensive moorland, where the sheep feed in favoured patches, such as areas of newly regenerating heather and heather adjacent to areas of palatable grassland (Grant et al. 1976; Gimingham 1971). This local concentration of grazing tends to result in these areas being over-utilised and suffering damage whilst other areas are neglected so that they grow almost unchecked and age normally.

A patchwork of small burns is usually recommended. Grouse are best served by long narrow strips no wider than 30 m and covering an area no greater than 2 ha (Gimingham 1971) and preferably about 0.5-1 ha (Grant & Milne 1981; Gimingham 1972). A patchwork of widely scattered small burns will attract sheep and so spread their grazing to most of the moorland. In an experiment in the west of Ireland, increased lamb production was obtained from moorland burned in patches up to 5 ha in size (Lance & Triggs 1974; Lance 1983).

The fraction of the farm or estate to be burnt each year obviously should equal the proportion of the burning regime period represented by one year. The combination of small individual fires and large total area means that over 1,000 fires are theoretically needed each season on some of the larger upland estates (Hobbs & Gimingham 1987), and it is apparent that limited manpower would make this impractical for most sheep farms (Braid & Tervet 1937; Grant & Milne 1981; Topham 1985).

Comprehensive guidelines for muirburn are presented in the Muirburn Working Party's (1977) booklet entitled A guide to good muirburn practice, and the advice given there is still appropriate.

Effects of burning on other moorland dominants

Because there is a long tradition of muirburn, most surviving moorland species are probably those adapted to rotational muirburn management. A succession of dominance has been recorded as moorland recovers from fire (Gimingham 1972, 1981).

Molinia caerulea is liable to dominate after fire on suitable damp substrates with lateral water movement (Ball 1974). It is resistant to fire because most of the buds are below the level to which fires penetrate tussocks (Grant, Hunter & Cross 1963). Where M. caerulea is dominant, graziers tend to burn the grassland annually in order to produce edible and digestible vegetation, as the unpalatable deciduous leaf litter hides the edible young shoots (Miles 1971). This regime perpetuates M. caerulea (McVean & Ratcliffe 1962; Grant, Hunter & Cross 1963), and debilitates heather (Currall 1981). The practice of burning grassland dominated by M. caerulea has been questioned (Grant, Hunter & Cross 1963; Miles 1971), but a long burning rotation may benefit heather, where it is still present (Grant, Hunter & Cross 1963). If it is not burned or grazed regularly, M. caerulea can form large tussocks which may be very difficult to use or remove.

Eriophorum vaginatum dominates temporarily after fire in blanket bog and assumes permanent dominance if the community is burnt frequently (Rawes & Hobbs 1979; Hobbs 1984). Rubus chamaemorus may dominate initially on blanket bog after fire, by extensive spread of underground rhizomes (Hobbs 1984), but is succeeded by heather (Taylor & Marks 1970) during long intervals between fires. Erica tetralix may also behave in this way (Gimingham 1972).

On drier substrates Erica cinerea and the rhizomatous species Vaccinium myrtillus and V. vitis-idaea (Gimingham 1972) are often temporarily abundant or dominant after fire but are gradually suppressed by the regrowth of Calluna. Frequent fires reduce the degree of suppression achieved by the Calluna and can allow these species to attain lasting dominance.

GRAZING

Heather and sheep

Heather is an evergreen shrub and the shoots produced in the spring remain green far longer than any other vegetation on the hill (Welch 1984a), providing herbage in the winter when very little alternative vegetation is available (Hunter 1954; Rawes & Williams 1973; Grant et al. 1978; Hobbs & Gimingham 1987). Hill grasses retain little palatable biomass in winter. Although heather is relatively unpalatable in summer and has relatively low nutritional value, it does have high value as winter feed (MAFF 1966) and forms the basis of the diet of sheep in winter (Grant et al. 1976). It is a rich source of minerals, especially copper and cobalt (Grant & Milne 1981). In one study, heather constituted 40% of the rumen contents of sheep sampled during winter, but only 20% during the summer, when more palatable and digestible species are available (MacLeod 1955). In summer, grazing tends to be restricted to the extreme tips of new growth (MacLeod 1955). On average, only 5-15% of the annual dry matter produced is utilised (Grant & Milne 1981). 500 kg of the annual dry matter produced by heather may be eaten by a 50 kg ewe in a year (Eadie 1970a).

The nutritive value and digestibility of the shoots are lower in the winter (33% dry matter digestible) (Thorsteinsson & Olafson 1965; Grant & Milne 1981) than in summer (60-65% digestible) (Rawes & Williams 1973; Welch 1984b). The live body weight of sheep may decrease during winter on the hill and is certainly not maintained if breeding ewes are fed solely on a heather diet during lactation and prior to mating (Grant & Milne 1973, 1981). Heather is most vulnerable to grazing at these times, especially during the autumn when both its carbohydrate reserves and overwintering shoots will be damaged (Grant, Bolton & Torvell 1981). Therefore, both sheep and heather benefit if the sheep are moved to more productive inbye land during these critical periods.

Burning increases the nutritional value of heather by stimulating new growth. Grazing (Grant 1971a; Welch 1984b) and clipping (Milne, Bagley & Grant 1979) can have a similar effect. Areas of new growth are grazed preferentially by sheep (Grant & Hunter 1968). The mosaic of heather stands that results from the patchwork burning recommended for grouse management encourages sheep to rake over a heft. This dispersal of sheep over a hill is not encouraged by the practice, often employed by graziers, of burning a few large areas.

Sheep concentrate in newly burnt areas (Grant & Hunter 1968), especially at lower grazing densities (Job & Taylor 1978), and damage the vegetation, whilst neglecting it elsewhere. Local concentration of heather grazing will also occur near grassy areas (Grant et al. 1976) and patches of palatable or reseeded grassland. Heather that is mixed with Agrostis/ Festuca or Deschampsia flexuosa grassland is more likely to be eaten than heather that is mixed with grasses of poor forage value such as Molinia caerulea and Nardus stricta. Local variations in grazing density are also affected by altitude, aspect, rainfall, soil wetness and pH, as these in turn affect the productivity of the vegetation and so limit carrying capacity.

Other moorland dominants

Heather occurs in mixtures with other species and in mosaics with other vegetation types. The palatability of these other species, which may vary through the year, may affect grazing on the heather.

On drier soils _Agrostis_ and _Festuca_ species form the most palatable upland grassland. This grassland considerably increases the number of sheep that an upland grazing unit can support without damaging the dwarf shrubs, but it also attracts grazing animals, sometimes leading to local damage, where they have free range. Rawes & Heal (1978) observed a grazing density of 0.5 sheep/ha on part of Moor House National Nature Reserve that contained approximately 1% _Agrostis/Festuca_ grassland, whereas 0.2 sheep/ha were observed on another part with no palatable grassland. These grasses are palatable throughout the year, but growth stops in winter (and reduces from late summer), limiting their contribution to the diet.

Bristle grasses with round leaves are less palatable than types like _Agrostis canina_ with flat leaves. _Deschampsia flexuosa_ has round leaves, and Grant _et al_. (1976) found that this was grazed mainly during May to July, although Hunter (1962) found that grassland dominated by this species is also eaten in winter, as _D. flexuosa_ is evergreen.

Nardus stricta is another round-leaved grass and one of the least palatable graminoids (Dale 1973), as its leaves are deficient in minerals (Ministry of Agriculture, Fisheries and Food 1966). It is grazed in late winter and early spring when other vegetation is scarce (Welch 1986). However, grazing is limited, as new growth is protected to some extent by the previous year's dead leaves, which are retained in the tussock (Nicholson, Paterson & Currie 1970).

The green stems of _Vaccinium myrtillus_ are grazed mainly in winter, although the plant is leafless then. It has a similar feeding value to heather and provides a rich source of minerals to grazing animals (MAFF 1966), although it is much less palatable than grasses and so scarcely eaten when they are available. Like heather, _Erica tetralix_ is grazed mainly in winter (MacLeod 1955; Welch 1984a).

On blanket bog, _Eriophorum vaginatum_, with heather, forms most of the sheep diet during winter (Grant _et al_. 1976). It is also favoured in early spring, when the flower stems (which have similar digestibility values to rye grass (Hunter 1962; Grant _et al_. 1987)) and the leaf bases (which are rich in phosphorus (Ministry of Agriculture, Fisheries & Food 1966)) emerge from the dead tussocks. It is grazed in late summer in preference to heather as productivity of more palatable grasses falls (Rawes & Williams 1973). Grazing can result in the production of more palatable, younger leaves (Chapin 1980). _Eriophorum angustifolium_ is also grazed in late summer (Grant _et al_. 1976).

Juncus squarrosus is less palatable to sheep than other graminoids but is grazed more readily by cattle and horses (Welch 1966). It may be richer in minerals than _Nardus stricta_ (Ministry of Agriculture, Fisheries & Food 1966). It is only grazed in late autumn, winter and early spring when more palatable vegetation is scarce (Grant & Campbell 1978; Welch 1984a).

The new growth of _Molinia caerulea_ is very digestible between May and July (Job & Taylor 1978; Welch 1984a) and is readily grazed then. Fresh growth of _Molinia_ has the feeding value of cultivated grasses but a lower calcium content (MAFF 966). Summer grazing is only readily available if the leaf litter is burnt every year (Miles 1971) or if the tussocks are grazed intensively in the spring (Grant, Hunter & Cross 1963). It is deciduous and so does not provide grazing in the winter (Grant, Hunter & Cross 1963). Cattle may graze Molinia in preference to heather (Hunter 1958). This species is cut for hay in summer on the continent (Ellenberg 1988) and still, very locally, in Wales.

The flowers of Rubus chamaemorus are readily removed by animals in summer (Taylor & Marks 1970). Trichophorum cespitosum is grazed as the young leaves appear and elongate in late spring and early summer (MAFF 1966; Welch 1984a) when the leaves are highly digestible; this digestibility declines rapidly (Grant et al. 1976) and the plant provides no food in winter.

The less palatable graminoids are all grazed mainly in the spring, when they bear fresh growth. In summer, if sheep can range freely on the hill, they congregate in and around the areas with palatable grasses and sedges, but are more evenly dispersed in autumn and winter, when they graze mainly heather. If reseeded pastures or Agrostis/Festuca grasslands are available, these are most usefully integrated into the grazing programme through the two pasture system recommended by the Hill Farming Research Organisation (now the Macaulay Land Use Research Institute) (Cunningham 1979; Davies 1984), i.e. they should be fenced and used only when herbage quality is most important to the sheep. With the use of this system, lamb production can be raised considerably, yet damage to heather may be reduced.

Grazing densities

It is well known by land managers that grazing animals can eliminate heather even from dry upland heather moor. Unfortunately existing research has not established how to determine the minimum density of animals that will cause this loss on a particular moorland. This is the crucial figure for a voluntary management agreement on moorland where heather loss is occurring. There have been only two important studies which offer guidance. Small paddocks were established on heather moorland at Glensaugh in Grampian Region (Grant 1971; Grant et al. 1978). Shoot production was maintained at the lower grazing density applied (about 2.7 ewes/ha) but cover and standing crop declined to some extent.

The other major study is that by Welch (1984b). He related changes in heather cover at 32 sample points on open moorland to a relative measure of the grazing intensity occurring there (volume of dung). It is possible to estimate stocking densities equivalent to the observed assessment of herbivore use at the sample points and therefore to suggest that heather cover declined at a local density of 2.7 ewes/ha where the measured variables fit the mean values found in these samples. Welch measured the effect of red grouse, red deer and cattle, and so was able to analyse the impact of these herbivores too; heather was estimated to decline at stocking rates of cattle above 0.2/ha.

Lance (1987) has widened the scope of Welch's regression analysis to make it potentially more applicable to other parts of Britain. Welch found that heather performance in his sites had a positive correlation with increasing altitude. Yet heather certainly grows less well at high altitude, so Welch suggests that decreased competition with other plants at higher altitudes must have affected his results. Lance uses other data linking heather production with altitude to derive an alternative to the growth index for use in Welch's equations. Lance suggests that removing this anomalous aspect of Welch's analysis indicates that heather can support fewer sheep without loss of cover. Where Welch suggests that heather declines above a stocking rate of 2.7 sheep/ha at his average heather growth of 4.7 cm/year, Lance's analysis suggests that the density should be only 1.82 sheep/ha. This considerable discrepancy needs to be resolved.

In drafting a voluntary agreement for heather moorland conservation, the need is to establish an acceptable herbivore density on a particular moorland grazing unit. Most such units consist of mixed vegetation - dry moorland, blanket bog and grasslands. The appropriate number of sheep depends on this mix of vegetation. Grasslands are productive and palatable (some types more so than others) and increase the potential to support stock, in summer at least, without the stock being forced to graze the heather. Further, the recent management of the heather-dominated components may significantly affect grazing potential; extensive stands of old heather are less productive, tend to discourage grazing by sheep and are particularly vulnerable to damage if grazed. Young (i.e. recently burned) stands are productive, relatively nutritious and more heavily grazed where sheep can follow their preference. The presence of extensive stands of old heather on a grazing unit of moorland will obviously increase the grazing pressure on other parts.

Welch's study deals with open moorland grazings, and the behaviour of the animals was not manipulated. However, no link is offered between the plot estimates of herbivore density and the overall stocking densities on the studied moorlands. This was a sensible approach for Welch as there are fewer variables involved in a study of the relationship between heather cover and grazing cover on individual plots; in particular, the external variables that may influence the grazing impact on the plot could be ignored. But neither Welch nor Lance can suggest how to determine an acceptable density of animals, given the variability in grazing potential between real moorland grazing units. Theoretically it would be possible, on a newly established moorland nature reserve, to establish from a number of plots whether herbivore use was above the limits predicted to maintain heather cover by Welch's analysis. If the acceptable limits were exceeded, the number of herbivores could be reduced and usage reassessed, and this process repeated until herbivore use was within the limits suggested to maintain heather cover. However, most landowners will expect a less cumbersome approach to reaching an agreement.

Grant's experiments on Glensaugh were a very valuable investigation of the relationship between sheep grazing and the maintenance of heather productivity, but it seems that we can extrapolate reliably from these relatively small enclosures to larger moorland units, even in that part of Britain. The usual mix of vegetation was largely absent (and even suppressed by herbicides) and it is reasonable to suspect that the sheep grazed the area more evenly than they would have done if not restrained in a small area for a short period of intensive grazing.

A new approach to address this problem has been to develop a computer model which enables simple parameters from entire moorland grazing units (including the areas of vegetation types) to be used to predict appropriate numbers of sheep, based on estimates of productivity, sheep intake and the capacity of heather to sustain grazing (Sibbald et al. 1987). However, the model as a whole has not been tested, so this approach is only indirectly supported by research. Further, although the model is designed for maintaining the productivity of the heather on the grazing unit, it cannot necessarily be assumed that this will result in heather cover or structure that is best for wildlife conservation or for its effects on other species. Nevertheless, if validated, this model would clearly be a valuable tool for conservation land managers trying to assess the grazing potential of heather moorland.

More studies have been published about heather-dominated blanket bog than about dry heather moorland. Heather on this waterlogged substrate is much less productive and reduction in heather cover or standing crop has been recorded in all observations and experiments with densities above about 1.3 ewes/ha (Hewson 1977; Rawes & Hobbs 1979; Grant, Bolton & Torvell 1981). However, again the applicability of these figures is difficult to assess, for they are derived from small enclosures or lack information about the mixture of vegetation so affected or both. The cover of heather increased when sheep were excluded from high altitude blanket bog (Rawes 1983). However, in this case although the overall density of sheep on the total moorland was 0.44/ha (summer grazing only), the density of sheep grazing on the blanket bog before exclosure was observed to be only 0.01-0.30 sheep/ha.

The vulnerability of heather on blanket bog to grazing damage is, perversely, one reason for maintaining burning there. In the north Pennines in particular, blanket bog has commonly been burned in rotation by keepers. This is apparently unnecessary, as unmanaged heather on blanket bog can rejuvenate naturally by burial of the stems in growing Sphagnum, so maintaining production. However, the heather on unburned blanket bog can grow tall and dense enough to discourage sheep from grazing on the bog. A network of recently burned stands attracts the sheep onto the bog and so may reduce grazing pressure on other parts of the estate, such as stands of dry heather moor and the more accessible fringes of the blanket bog. The balance must be struck between the adverse effects of rotational burning (in many cases an established practice) and the impact of grazing on the heather moorland of the entire estate. The possibility of extensive accidental fires on neglected blanket bog has already been discussed (p. 9).

There is some evidence that sheep are more efficient in lamb production at lower stocking rates. At Rede Valley in Northumberland, lamb production reached its maximum at a stocking density of 1.2 sheep/ha unless part of the hill was sacrificed to improved pasture (Davies 1984). Lippert, Milne & Russell (1982) also demonstrated that the highest weight of lamb is produced at 1.2 sheep/ha.

The impact of other herbivores

Cattle must be expected to inflict more damage on heather than sheep, both by mechanical damage from trampling and because they are less selective when feeding. Welch (1984b) has estimated that a density of 0.2 cattle/ha can cause a decline in heather cover in his study area in north-east Scotland.

There are only scattered herds of feral goats today. However, domestic stock were once abundant in the uplands (Williams 1983) and could be again, as over the past decade goats have become very profitable in New Zealand. As a result some Scottish graziers are attempting to breed hardy goats with good quality cashmere, but the immediate consequence of this has been that many feral herds have declined as animals have been taken for use as breeding stock. It has been suggested that their different grazing preferences might enable goats to be used to improve pasture quality for sheep (Grant et al. 1984). A greater threat to upland wildlife conservation would be that their agility allows them to gain access to cliff ledges (Corbet & Southern 1977) which are presently an important refuge for tall herb communities and to a wider variety of shrubs (Ratcliffe 1977). Their small body size and their small incisors enable them to select nutritious food from low-quality herbage. On Rhum, heather is an important part of their diet in winter (September to April, with heaviest use in October and November) (Gordon et al. 1987).

The staple diet of red grouse is heather, and a single grouse will consume 70 g daily (Rawes & Williams 1973; Rawes & Heal 1978), but only 5% of the annual dry matter produced is eaten by grouse (Hobbs & Gimingham 1987). The controlled burning of moors, but not necessarily of blanket bogs (Hobbs 1984), produces a fairly stable grouse population, although regular cyclic variations continue (Watson & Moss 1979). Grouse avoid newly burnt areas for up to three years (Watson & Moss 1972), when very little heather is available. Estimates of density are usually related to territory size, which varies from 0.2-13.2 ha but is mostly 2-5 ha (Watson & Miller 1971).

Heather is an important food of mountain hares, and young heather is preferentially grazed in summer (Hewson 1976; Moss & Hewson 1985). Building and mature heather is grazed in the winter and spring (Hewson 1976). Heavy grazing by maintain hares may result in a distinctive form of heather, as lateral branching is increased. These laterals root adventitiously and the bushes that result are flat and circular. Hares can maintain old heather in a 'young' state (Welch & Kemp 1973; Welch & Scott 1985) but are only likely to modify small parts of moorland in this way and their populations are now only dense in north-east Scotland.

Heather may constitute up to 10% of the diet of ponies in winter (Nature Conservancy Council 1983). They may, like cattle, also damage heather by trampling, because their size enables them to walk through tall heather quite easily. Ponies are selective feeders and can graze close to the ground. As a result they are able to feed from the good Agrostis/Festuca grasslands on Rhum even in winter and take little heather there throughout the year (Gordon et al. 1987).

Heather is grazed preferentially by red deer, especially in the winter (Hobson 1970; Hewson 1976; Grant, Hamilton & Souter 1981). They eat more heather than sheep, especially in the summer (Hobson 1970). Red deer prefer to graze older heather, probably because it is taller, and neglect pioneer stands (Hewson 1976; Moss, Welch & Rothery 1981; Hobbs & Gimingham 1987). As older heather is less productive than young, red deer may thus damage heather more readily than sheep (Hobson 1970). Deer kept in paddocks at a stocking density of 2.0 hind-equivalents/ha reduced heather cover, whereas a stocking density of 1.34 hind-equivalents/ha did not (Grant, Bolton & Torvell 1981).

Hobbs & Gimingham (1987) suggest that overgrazing by red deer is not generally a problem because stocking rates are comparatively low at 0.1 deer/ha (Mitchell, Staines & Welch 1977). However, Stewart (1985) suggests that deer densities may reach 0.31 deer/ha locally and that numbers have increased considerably recently, e.g. by 154% in the East Grampians since 1966 (Staines & Ratcliffe 1987). Nicholson (1970) has observed that red deer congregate in valleys during the winter, where they may cause local conversion of heather-dominated vegetation to grasslands.

Intense grazing by red deer can result in dominance by <u>Deschampsia</u>, <u>cespitosa</u> and <u>Festuca</u> <u>rubra</u> (Ball 1974) or <u>D</u>. <u>flexuosa</u> with <u>Vaccinium</u> <u>myrtillus</u> (Grant, Bolton & Torvell 1981).

We have only considered here the impact of herbivores on heather. Other species of plant are also affected by grazing, although critical herbivore densities are likely to be different from those for heather. In addition there are likely to be knock-on effects on animal populations. The picture is further complicated by changes in the competitive interactions between species, in which heather, a successful dominant, is likely to play a major part.

DISCUSSION

Valuable research has been carried out, particularly by Grant at the Hill Farming Research Organisation and Welch at the Institute of Terrestrial Ecology, to determine the relationship between grazing and heather. From this we can suggest that the local density of sheep (i.e. the density on pure heather moorland in a paddock or on a plot on open moorland) must be maintained below about 2.7 sheep/ha or heather cover will decline. However, a useful reanalysis of Welch's data by Lance (1987) suggests that this figure may need to be revised down to 1.8 sheep/ha (and below this where heather growth is slower). On blanket bog, where heather is less productive, the limit is even lower than this. However, most authors have recorded that grazing at low densities benefits heather growth. The main exception is high altitude blanket bog, where gains in cover have been suggested when sheep ranging at very low densities (less than 0.4 sheep/ha) were excluded.

Unfortunately the literature does not yet link local density with real numbers on complete moorland grazing units. Such units almost invariably contain a mixture of vegetation in addition to heather-dominated types. Grasslands, in particular, will have a considerable effect on the carrying capacity of the unit and hence its ability to support grazing animals without loss of heather. The age and type of heather (i.e. whether on soil or peat) may also have a considerable modifying effect.

The Macaulay Land Use Research Institute (MLURI) has recently developed a simple computer model to predict the maximum number of sheep that can be kept on a hill grazing unit where heather moorland predominates (Sibbald et al. 1987). This model calculates the potential productivity of the moorland based on the areas of three age-classes of heather and three classes of grassland (inbye, good and poor) and then estimates consumption by different size-classes of sheep. This pragmatic approach appears to be very useful and is to be developed further.

The impact of other herbivores could easily be incorporated in the MLURI model. Wild red deer are present in considerable and increasing numbers in the Highlands. Changing economics may make cattle and goats more important than they are at present. Ponies are a considerable factor on many moorlands in south-west England and on Shetland. Wethers are believed to feed less selectively than ewes and lambs (Roberts 1959; Welch 1966) and may limit the spread of less palatable grasses into hill grasslands. They may be important for sheep-grazed upland nature reserves where income from lambing and subsidies is a secondary consideration. The model also needs to be able to take into account the considerable variations in the numbers of animals that can occur seasonally on some moorlands. In particular, summer-only stocking regimes are common in many parts of the country and may increase as more sheep are housed in winter. Heather is grazed mainly in winter, but can be eaten in summer (especially as grass production falls after mid-year) where stocking rates are high. On SSSIs the effect of sheep on heather could be reduced by preventing winter grazing if safe limits for summer grazing were established.

The model depends on production estimates for the heather types which have not been widely measured but are likely to be affected by factors such as altitude, position and soil nutrient availablility as well as heather age (Grant & Milne 1981). It also uses the results of paddock experiments in north-east Scotland which suggested that heather productivity was maintained with 40% removal of green shoot production. This may be a reasonable assumption, but the variability with location is unknown. However, for many estates, the amount and type of grassland may be overwhelmingly important. Once again, the variation with location is little known and the effects of differences caused by species composition may be very important so that the definition of the 'good grass' category, the most productive component of the unimproved vegetation, may need to be refined.

Although in the model the contribution from heather is limited to 40% of its estimated total production, this does not necessarily prevent the recommended sheep numbers from removing more than this proportion in reality. On sites with a large area of heather, the model will set a relatively low number of sheep, because it assumes that 50% of their diet is grass. Here, heather production will be in surplus and the sheep are likely to eat much less than their permitted 40%. But where the area of heather on the site is relatively small, even though sheep numbers are still limited by total production, the much higher ratio of sheep to heather may result in more than 40% of heather production being consumed, especially in winter when grass production is low and heather remains edible. Even in summer, the combination of sheep at high density and heather in small relict blocks appears to lead to rapid losses of heather. The most crucial next stage, if the model is to be used to maintain heather as well as maximise sheep production, is to test that loss of heather cover does not occur on estates stocked with the number of sheep recommended by the model and to establish how the model can be modified to prevent losses where they occur.

The model assumes that the burning regime will be adjusted to maintain all the heather young (except on blanket bog). This restricted range of heather structure is not sufficient for optimum wildlife conservation. Stands of older heather are used by raptorial birds for breeding and are associated with a flora and invertebrate fauna that may include a more diverse assemblage of characteristic moorland species. Some stands of heather should be protected from burning. It may be sufficient to allow these to develop where burning is inadvisable on steeper slopes and in gills and cleuchs which are particularly liable to erosion. However, there is an obvious need here for wildlife potential to be defined more clearly. What are the effects of differing proportions of heather in the total mosaic of vegetation and of differing proportions of the structural range found in heather-dominated vegetation? Extensive stands of less productive old heather, for instance, may increase the grazing pressure on more productive stands of heather, leading to losses there. The value of different mixtures of different ages of heather-dominated vegetation needs to be known.

The literature on burning leads to the conclusion that, generally, heather stands should be burned when they are about 20-30 cm tall. On most heather moor this will result in a rotation of, at most, 10-15 years. Long-term monitoring at Moor House National Nature Reserve has established that blanket bog should probably not be burned more than once in 20 years, and it is generally accepted that the heather on bog need not be burned at all as the stems are buried by Sphagnum growth and so regenerate naturally. However, in many areas blanket bog has been burned on rotation by keepers. The density of sheep on some upland estates is such that active use of the bogs by sheep may need to be encouraged by producing accessible areas for them by burning. It is necessary to consider sheep numbers and the production of all the vegetation of the grazing unit, for instance using the MLURI model, before removing consent to burn.

The literature suggests that areas burned should be small, ideally less than 2 ha, for sheep and red grouse alike. Long narrow strips about 30 m wide benefit grouse, encourage sheep to feed throughout the moor and act as good fire-breaks to help prevent extensive accidental fires which are likely to be harmful to wildlife. Heather is a powerful dominant and if conditions are very favourable it may overwhelm less vigorous plant species that normally grow with it and may invade and replace other moorland vegetation types. In the east of Britain, moorland that has been burned repeatedly is characteristically dominated by heather, to the almost total exclusion of other species. Thus good management to maintain heather and red grouse may not inevitably lead to conservation of the full range of moorland species. Most past studies of burning management have been concerned to maximise heather production rather than to maintain the full characteristic assemblage of plant species that contribute to heather moorland. It is now known that stands of old heather may regenerate vegetatively under the right conditions. They can develop a diverse age structure and a mixture of dwarf shrubs and possess a rich understorey of bryophytes and indicative moorland herbs such as Listera cordata. However, these stands are little studied and their full significance for conservation management is not yet known. The conclusion must be that the maintenance of most heather-dominated moorland depends upon management by burning on a suitable rotation and that this is particularly true where grazing is at modern commercial densities.

On SSSIs, management incompatible with heather maintenance can be prevented through a voluntary agreement under Section 15 of the Countryside Act 1968, but there is a need for greater experience of practical implementation of techniques and methods to maintain heather cover. Constructing a voluntary agreement may require the provision of alternatives more tempting than a simple reduction of stock. Fortunately, it may be as important to encourage shepherding or appropriate annual burning as it is to control sheep numbers. Changing the grazing season, for instance by making it possible to remove more of the ewes at lambing and tupping time, may also achieve more than making a small reduction in the total number of sheep. Improving moorland, or even run-down marginal fields, must be assumed to reduce the wildlife potential of the improved area but might be appropriate if these areas are not within the SSSI and if this prevents damage to it.

The cost of manpower for burning may mean that support is required in the form of temporary trained help or cash help to adopt less labour-intensive but more expensive techniques such as foam-spraying or mowing. Heather moorland is already mowed by National Park Authorities and the NCC, but very little systematic work is under way on successful methods or their impact. Best regeneration has been obtained with the use of forage harvesters on the North York Moors (Quest 1987). The cheaper flail mowers have produced good results elsewhere, but the mulch of chopped heather debris can prevent regeneration. Even very finely chopped debris might affect heather adversely by recycling nutrients normally lost to a greater extent in burning. More research on methods and consequences needs to be carried out urgently, for mowing is a promising substitute and adjunct to traditional burning management. The NCC has little experience of helping landholders with their heather burning, but the Forestry Commission has developed at least one experienced team which helps its neighbours with muirburn very effectively (although with a different motive).

In many cases, help to develop shepherding or burning may be most crucial in the initial stages. It is easier to carry out controlled burning of moorland safely where the moorland is subdivided by recently burned heather. Similarly, once sheep are used to being shepherded, they may move along their accustomed paths as soon as they see the shepherd's landrover or hear him whistling, so that he may not have to walk the whole route each day. Appropriate burning will benefit red grouse and so extra income from shooting could replace the need for external help or cash once the moor is well burned.

In the long term it is important that simple techniques applicable to whole moorlands are available. It may be possible on SSSIs to manipulate heather cover locally by using extra fencing and restoration techniques, but this is time-consuming and expensive. Such techniques are unlikely to be practicable even for improved Environmentally Sensitive Area agreements and certainly not for the wider upland environment, of which only about 15% is protected as SSSIs. A better understanding of the relationship between grazing animals, management and moorland is required to prevent and reverse the losses of wildlife that have occurred from Britain's moorlands in recent decades.

ACKNOWLEDGEMENTS

We thank Angus Macdonald and Helen Armstrong for their contributions to this work and Dr D B A Thompson for his unremitting encouragement.

REFERENCES

ALLEN, S.E. 1964. Chemical aspects of heather burning. Journal of Applied Ecology, 1, 347-367.

ANDERSON, P., & YALDEN, D.W. 1981. Increased sheep numbers and the loss of heather moorland in the Peak district, England. Biological Conservation, 20, 195-213.

BALL. D.F., DALE, J., SHEAIL, J., DICKSON, K.E., & WILLIAMS, W.M. 1981. Ecology of vegetation change in upland landscapes. Part 1. General synthesis. Bangor Occasional Paper No. 2. Bangor, I.T.E.

BALL, M.E. 1974. Floristic changes on grasslands and heaths on the Isle of Rhum after a reduction or exclusion of grazing. Journal of Environmental Management, 2, 299-318.

BIRKS, H.J.B. 1988. Long-term ecological change in the British uplands. In: Ecological change in the uplands, ed. by M.B. Usher & D.B.A. Thompson, 37-56. Oxford, Blackwell Scientific Publications.

BRAID, K.W., & TERVET, I.W. 1937. Certain botanical aspects of the dying-out of heather. Scottish Journal of Agriculture, 20, 365-372.

BUNCE, R.G.H., & BARR, C.J. 1988. The extent of land under different management regimes in the uplands and the potential for change. In: Ecological change in the uplands, ed. by M.B. Usher & D.B.A. Thompson, 415-426. Oxford, Blackwell Scientific Publications.

CHAPIN, F.S.III. 1980. Effects of clipping upon nutrient status and forage value of tundra plants in arctic Alaska. In: Proceedings of the 2nd International Reindeer/Caribou Symposium, Roros, Norway, 1979, ed. by E. Reimers, E. Gaare & S. Skjennsberg, 19-25.

CORBET, G.E., & SOUTHERN, H.M. 1977. The handbook of British mammals. Oxford, Blackwell Scientific Publications.

CUNNINGHAM, J.M.M. 1979. The role of agriculture and its relationship with other land uses. In: Forestry and farming in upland Britain. Forestry Commission Occasional Paper No. 6. B.A.A.S. 1979, 3-27. H.M.S.O.

CURRALL, J.E.P. 1981. Some effects of management by fire on wet heath vegetation in Western Scotland. PhD Thesis, University of Aberdeen.

DALE, J. 1973. Sheep grazing experiments in Snowdonia. Nature in Wales, 13, 229-234.

DALE, J., & HUGHES, R.E. 1978. Sheep population studies in relation to the Snowdonia environment. In: Production ecology of British moors and montane grasslands, ed. by O.W. Heal & D.F. Perkins, 348-353. Berlin, Springer-Verlag.

DAVIES, M.H. 1984. Long-term production in Dargues Hope blackface flocks. Redesdale EHF (ADAS) Annual Review, 43-48.

EADIE, J. 1970. Sheep production and pastoral resources. In: Animal populations in relation to their food resources, ed. by A. Watson, 7-24. Oxford, Blackwell Scientific Publications.

ELLENBERG, H. 1988. Vegetation ecology of Central Europe. Cambridge, Cambridge University Press.

EVANS, R. 1977. Overgrazing and soil erosion on hill pastures with particular reference to the Peak District. British Grassland Society. Journal, 32, 65-76.

FORREST, G.I. 1971. Structure and production of North Pennine blanket bog vegetation. Journal of Ecology, 59, 453-479.

GIMINGHAM, C.H. 1971. Calluna heathlands: use and conservation in the light of some ecological effects of management. In: The scientific management of animal and plant communities for conservation, ed. by E. Duffey & A.S. Watt, 91-103. Oxford, Blackwell Scientific Publications.

GIMINGHAM, C.H. 1972. Ecology of heathlands. London, Chapman and Hall.

GIMINGHAM, C.H. 1981. Moorland management: advances in the practical application of ecological research. Botanical Society of Edinburgh. Transactions , 43, 255-262.

GORDON, I., DUNBAR, R., BUCKLAND, D., & MILLER, D. 1987. Ponies, Cattle & Goats. In: Rhum: the natural history of an island, ed. by T. Clutton-Brock & M.E. Ball, 110-125. Edinburgh, Edinburgh University Press.

GRANT, S.A. 1968. Heather regeneration following burning: a survey. British Grassland Society. Journal, 23, 26-33.

GRANT, S.A. 1971. Interactions of grazing and burning on heather moors. 2. Effects on primary production and level of utilisation. British Grassland Society. Journal, 26, 173-181.

GRANT, S.A., BARTHRAM, G.T., LAMB, W.I.C., & MILNE, J.A. 1978. Effects of season and level of grazing on the utilisation of heather by sheep. 1. Responses of the sward. British Grassland Society. Journal, 33, 289-300.

GRANT, S.A., BOLTON, G.R., & RUSSELL, A.J.F. 1984. The utilisation of sown and indigenous plant species by sheep and goats grazing hill pastures. Grass and Forage Science, 39, 361-370.

GRANT, S.A., BOLTON, G.R., & TORVELL, L. 1981. The effects of grazing by sheep on the structure, stability and productivity of blanket bog. Hill Farming Research Organisation Biennial Report 1978-1981, 68-70.

GRANT, S.A., & CAMPBELL, D.R. 1978. Seasonal variation in in vitro digestibility and structural carbohydrate content of some commonly grazed plants of blanket bog. British Grassland Society. Journal, 33, 167-173.

GRANT, S.A., HAMILTON, W.J., & SOUTER, C. 1981. The responses of heather-dominated vegetation in north-east Scotland to grazing by red deer. Journal of Ecology, 69, 189-204.

GRANT, S.A., & HUNTER, R.F. 1968. Interactions of grazing and burning on heather moors and their implications in heather management. British Grassland Society. Journal, 23, 285-293.

GRANT, S.A., HUNTER, R.F., & CROSS, C. 1963. The effects of muirburning Molinia-dominant communities. British Grassland Society. Journal, 18, 249-257.

GRANT, S.A., LAMB, W.I.C., KERR, C.D., & BOLTON, G.R. 1976. The utilisation of blanket bog vegetation by grazing sheep. Journal of Applied Ecology, 13, 857-869.

GRANT, S.A., & MILNE, J.A. 1973. Factors affecting the role of heather (Calluna vulgaris L. Hull) in grazing systems. In: Hill pasture improvement and its economic utilisation, 41-46. Potassium Institute Ltd., Colloquium Proceedings No.3.

GRANT, S.A., & MILNE, J.A. 1981. Heather management. Blackface Journal, 33, 13-17.

GRANT, S.A., MILNE, J.A., BARTHRAM, G.T., & SOUTER, W.G. 1982. Effects of season and level of grazing on the utilisation of heather by sheep. 3. Longer-term responses and sward recovery. Grass and Forage Science, 37, 311-320.

GRANT, S.A., TORVELL, L., SMITH, H.K., SUCKLING, D.E., FORBES, T.D.A., & HODGSON, J. 1987. Comparative studies of diet selection by sheep and cattle: blanket bog and heather moor. Journal of Ecology, 75, 947-960.

HEWSON, R. 1976. Grazing by mountain hares Lepus timidus L., red deer Cervus elaphus L. and red grouse Lagopus l. scoticus on heather moorland in north-east Scotland. Journal of Applied Ecology, 13, 657-666.

HEWSON, R. 1977. The effect on heather Calluna vulgaris of excluding sheep from moorland in north-east England. Naturalist, 102, 133-136.

HILL FARMING RESEARCH ORGANISATION, 1979. Science and hill farming: twenty-five years of work at the Hill Farming Research Organisation 1954-1979. Penicuik.

HOBBS, R.J. 1984. Length of burning rotation and community composition in high-level Calluna-Eriophorum bog in N. England. Vegetatio, 57, 129-136.

HOBBS, R.J., & GIMINGHAM, C.H. 1987. Vegetation, Fire and Herbivore Interactions in Heathland. Advances in Ecological Research, 16, 87-193.

HOBSON, P.N. 1970. Some field experiments on the rumen functions of red deer, hill sheep and reindeer. Deer, 2, 450-453.

HUNTER, R.F. 1954. The grazing of hill pasture sward types. Journal of the British Grassland Society, 9, 195-208.

HUNTER, R.F. 1958. Hill land improvement. Advancement of Science, 15, 194-196.

HUNTER, R.F. 1962. Hill sheep and their pasture: a study of sheep-grazing in south-east Scotland. Journal of Ecology, 50, 651-680.

JENKINS, J.D. 1971. Heather beetle (Lochmaea suturalis). Game Conservancy Annual Review, 2, 66-70.

JOB, D.A., & TAYLOR, J.A. 1978. The production, utilisation and management of upland grazings on Plynlimon, Wales. Journal of Biogeography, 5, 173-191.

KAY, R.N.B., & STAINES, B.W. 1981. The nutrition of red deer (Cervus elaphus). Nutrition Abstracts Review, B 51, 601-622.

KENWORTHY, J.B. 1963. Temperatures in heather burning. Nature, 200, 1226.

KENWORTHY, J.B. 1964. A study of the changes in plant and soil nutrients associated with moor burning and grazing. PhD Thesis, University of St Andrews.

LANCE, A.N. 1983. Performance of sheep on unburned and serially burned blanket bog in western Ireland. Journal of Applied Ecology, 20, 767-775.

LANCE, A.N. 1987. Estimating acceptable stocking levels for heather moorland. In: Agriculture and conservation in the hills and uplands, ed. by M. Bell & G.H. Bunce, 109-115. Grange-over-Sands, Institute of Terrestrial Ecology.

LANCE, A.N., & TRIGGS, R. 1974. Developing hill bogland to benefit both grouse and sheep. Farm and Food Research, 5, 135-136.

LIPPERT, M., MILNE, J.A., & RUSSEL, A.J.F. 1982. The feeding of ewes in mid pregnancy. Animal Production, 34, 383. (British Society of Animal Production, Winter Meeting 1982.)

LOVAT, Lord. 1911. Moorland management and heather burning. In: The grouse in health and in disease, ed. by A.S. Leslie, 372-413. London, Smith, Elder & Co.

MacLEOD, A.C. 1955. Heather in the seasonal diet of sheep. Proceedings of the British Society of Animal Production, 13-17.

McVEAN, D.N., & LOCKIE, J.D. 1969. Ecology and land use in upland Scotland. Edinburgh, Edinburgh University Press.

McVEAN, D.N., & RATCLIFFE, D.A. 1962. Plant communities of the Scottish highlands: a study of Scottish mountain, moorland and forest vegetation. London, H.M.S.O. (Nature Conservancy Council Monograph No. 1.)

MALTBY, E. 1980. The impact of severe fire on Calluna moorland. Bulletin d'Ecologie, 7, 683-708.

MILES, J. 1971. Burning Molinia-dominant vegetation for grazing by red deer. British Grassland Society. Journal, 26, 247-250.

MILLER, G.R. 1966. Botanical studies. Nature Conservancy Unit of Grouse and Moorland Ecology Progress Report, 12, 20-26.

MILLER, G.R., KINNAIRD, J.W., & CUMMINS, R.P. 1978. Woodland regeneration on red deer range. Institute of Terrestrial Ecology Annual Report, 65-66.

MILLER, G.R., & MILES, J. 1970. Regeneration of heather (Calluna vulgaris (L.) Hull) at different ages and seasons in north-east Scotland. Journal of Applied Ecology, 7, 51-60.

MILLER, G.R., MILES, J., & HEAL, O.W. 1984. Moorland management: a study of Exmoor. Cambridge, Institute of Terrestrial Ecology.

MILLER, G.R., WATSON, A., & JENKINS, D.J. 1970. Responses of red grouse populations to experimental improvement of their food. In: Animal populations in relation to their food resources ed. by A. Watson, 323-335. Oxford, Blackwell Scientific Publications.

MILNE, J.A., BAGLEY, L., & GRANT, S.A. 1979. Effects of season and level of grazing on the utilisation of heather by sheep. 2. Diet selection and intake. Grass and Forage Science, 34, 45-53.

MINISTRY OF AGRICULTURE FISHERIES AND FOOD. 1966. Grass and Grassland. London, H.M.S.O. (MAFF Bulletin No. 154.)

MITCHELL, B., STAINES, B.W., & WELCH, D. 1977. Ecology of red deer: a research review relevant to their management in Scotland. Cambridge, Institute of Terrestrial Ecology.

MOSS, R., & HEWSON, R. 1985. Effects on heather of heavy grazing by mountain hares. Holarctic Ecology, 8, 280-284.

MOSS, R., WELCH, D., & ROTHERY, P. 1981. Effects of grazing by mountain hares and red deer on the production and chemical composition of heather. Journal of Applied Ecology, 18, 487-496.

MUIRBURN WORKING PARTY 1977. A guide to good muirburn practice. Edinburgh, H.M.S.O.

NATURE CONSERVANCY COUNCIL 1983. The food and feeding behaviour of cattle and ponies in the New Forest. Lyndhurst, Nature Conservancy Council.

NATURE CONSERVANCY COUNCIL 1984. Nature conservation in Great Britain. Shrewsbury, Nature Conservancy Council.

NATURE CONSERVANCY COUNCIL 1986. Nature conservation and afforestation in Britain. Peterborough, Nature Conservancy Council.

NATURE CONSERVANCY COUNCIL 1987. Changes in the Cumbrian countryside. Peterborough, Nature Conservancy Council. (Research and survey in nature conservation, No. 6.)

NEWBOULD, P. 1974. The improvement of hill pastures for agriculture. A review, Part 1 and Part 2. British Grassland Society. Journal, 29, 241-247, 30, 41-44.

NEWBOULD, P. 1979. The limitations and potential for pasture production from the hills and uplands. In: Forestry and farming in upland Britain. Selected papers presented at the British Association for the Advancement of Science, 1979, 29-75. Edinburgh, Forestry Commission (Occasional Paper No. 6).

NICHOLSON, I.A. 1970. Some effects of animal grazing and browsing on vegetation. Botanical Society of Edinburgh. Transactions, 41, 85-94.

NICHOLSON, I.A., PATERSON, I.S., & CURRIE, A. 1970. A study of vegetational dynamics: selection by sheep and cattle in Nardus pasture. In: Animal populations in relation to their food resources, ed. by

A. Watson, 129-143. Oxford, Blackwell Scientific Publications. (British Ecological Society Symposium No. 10.)

PARRY, M., BRUCE, A., & HARKNESS, C. 1981. The plight of British moorlands. New Scientist, 28, 550-551.

PICOZZI, N. 1968. Grouse bags in relation to the management and geology of heather moors. Journal of Applied Ecology, 5, 483-488.

QUEST, P. 1987. The purple heart. Landscape Design, 165, 32-35.

RACKHAM, O. 1986. The history of the countryside. London, Dent.

RADLEY, J. 1965. Significance of major moorland fires. Nature, 205, 1254-1259.

RATCLIFFE, D.A., 1977. A nature conservation review. 2 vols. Cambridge, Cambridge University Press.

RATCLIFFE, D.A., & THOMPSON, D.B.A. 1988. The British uplands: their ecological character and international significance. In: Ecological change in the uplands, ed. by M.B. Usher & D.B.A. Thompson, 9-36. Oxford, Blackwell Scientific Publications.

RAWES, M., 1983. Changes in two high altitude blanket bogs after the cessation of sheep grazing. Journal of Ecology, 71, 219-235.

RAWES, M., & HEAL, O.W. 1978. The blanket bog as part of a Pennine moorland. In: Production ecology of British moors and mountain grasslands, ed. by O.W. Heal & D.F. Perkins, 224-243. Berlin, Springer-Verlag.

RAWES, M., & HOBBS, R. 1979. Management of semi-natural blanket bog in the northern Pennines. Journal of Ecology, 67, 789-807.

RAWES, M., & WELCH, D. 1969. Upland productivity of vegetation and sheep at the Moor House National Nature Reserve, Westmorland, England. Oikos, Supplement II.

RAWES, M., & WILLIAMS, R. 1973. Production and utilisation of Calluna and Eriophorum. In: Hill pasture improvement and its economic utilisation, 115-119. Potassium Institute Ltd. (Colloquium Proceedings No. 3.)

ROBERTS, R.A. 1959. Ecology of human occupation and land use in Snowdonia. Journal of Ecology, 47, 317-323.

ROYAL SOCIETY FOR THE PROTECTION OF BIRDS 1984. Hill farming and birds: a survival plan. Sandy, Royal Society for the Protection of Birds.

SIBBALD, A.R., GRANT, S.A., MILNE, J.A., & MAXWELL, T.J. 1987. Heather moorland management: a model. In: Agriculture and conservation in the hills and uplands, ed. M. Bell & R.G.H. Bunce, 107-108. Grange-over-Sands, ITE.

STAINES, B.W., & RATCLIFFE, P.R. 1987. Estimating the abundance of red deer (Cervus elaphus L.) and roe deer (Capreolus capreolus L.) and their current status in Great Britain. Zoological Society. Symposium, 58, 131-152.

STEWART, L.K. 1985. Red Deer. In: Vegetation management in northern Britain, ed. by R.B. Murray, 45-50. Croydon, BCPC Publications.

SYDES, C., & MILLER, G.R. 1988. Range management and nature conservation in the British uplands. In: Ecological change in the uplands, ed. by M.B. Usher & D.B.A. Thompson, 323-338. Oxford, Blackwell Scientific Publications.

TAYLOR, K., & MARKS, T.C. 1970. The influence of burning and grazing on the growth and development of Rubus chamaemorus L. and Calluna-Eriophorum bog. In: The scientific management of animal and plant communities for conservation, ed. by E. Duffey & A.S. Watt, 153-166. Oxford, Blackwell Scientific Publications.

THORNSTEINSSON, I., & OLAFSSON, G. 1965. The chemical composition and digestibility of some Icelandic range plants. Atvinnudeild Haskolans Rit Landbunadardeilder, (A), No. 17.

TINSLEY, H.M. 1975. The former woodland of the Nidderdale Moors (Yorkshire) and the role of early man in its decline. Journal of Ecology, 63, 1-16.

TOPHAM, M.R. 1985. Sheep numbers and heather conservation on common land in the north of England. University of Newcastle, Department of Agriculture and Food Marketing (Discussion Paper 9).

WATSON, A., & MILLER, G.R. 1971. Territory size and aggression in a fluctuating red grouse population. Journal of Animal Ecology, 40, 367-383.

WATSON, A., & MOSS, R. 1972. A current model of population dynamics in red grouse. In: Proceedings of the International Ornithological Congress, 15, 134-149. The Hague, Netherlands.

WATSON, A., & MOSS, R. 1979. Population studies in the Tetraonidae. Ornis Fennica, 56, 87-109.

WELCH, D., 1966. Biological flora of the British Isles: Juncus squarrosus L. Journal of Ecology, 54, 535-548.

WELCH, D., 1974. A history of the Moor House area. Aspects of the ecology of the northern Pennines, Occasional Paper No. 7, Report N.C. 163F.

WELCH, D. 1982. Dung properties and defecation characteristics in some Scottish herbivores, with an evaluation of the dung-volume method of assessing occupance. Acta Theriologica, 27, 191-212.

WELCH, D. 1984a. Studies in the grazing of heather moorland in north-east Scotland. I. Site descriptions and patterns of utilisation. Journal of Applied Ecology, 21, 179-195.

WELCH, D. 1984b. Studies in the grazing of heather moorland in north-east Scotland. II. Response of heather. Journal of Applied Ecology, 21, 297-207.

WELCH, D. 1984c. Studies in the grazing of heather moorland in north-east Scotland. III. Floristics. Journal of Applied Ecology, 21, 209-225.

WELCH, D. 1985. Studies in the grazing of heather moorland in north-east Scotland. IV. Seed dispersal and plant establishment in dung. Journal of Applied Ecology, 22, 461-471.

WELCH, D. 1986. Studies in the grazing of heather moorland in north east Scotland. V. Trends in Nardus stricta and other unpalatable graminoids. Journal of Applied Ecology, 23, 1047-1058.

WELCH, D., & KEMP, E. 1973. A Callunetum subjected to intensive grazing by mountain hares. Botanical Society of Edinburgh. Transactions, 42, 89-99.

WELCH, D., & RAWES, M. 1966. The intensity of sheep grazing on high level blanket bog in upper Teesdale. Irish Journal of Agricultural Research, 5, 185-196.

WELCH, D., & SCOTT, D. 1985. Further observations on a Callunetum intensively grazed by mountain hares (Lepus timidus L.). Botanical Society of Edinburgh. Transactions, 44, 321-333.

WILLIAMS, D.H. 1983. The Welsh Cistercians. Caldey Island, Cyhoeddiadau Sistersiaidd.

"Research & survey in nature conservation" series

No. 1   The use of permanent quadrats to record changes in the structure and composition of Wytham Woods, Oxfordshire. A S Horsfall and K J Kirby. 1985.

No. 2   Monitoring the abundance of butterflies 1976-1985. E Pollard, M L Hall and T J Bibby. 1986.

No. 3   Saltmarsh survey of Great Britain: Bibliography. Compiled by Kevin Charman, Wanda Fojt and Shirley Penny. 1986.

No. 4   A survey of the numbers and breeding distribution of the North Atlantic gannet Sula bassana and an assessment of the changes which have occurred since Operation Seafarer 1969/70. Sarah Wanless. 1987.

No. 5   Agricultural structures policy and nature conservation in Upland Grampian: a pilot study. J R Crabtree, Sue Evans, Brian J Revell and Philip M K Leat. 1987.

No. 6   Changes in the Cumbrian countryside. First report of the National Countryside Monitoring Scheme. 1987.

No. 7   The Wash and its environment. Report of a conference held on 8-10 April 1987 at Horncastle, Lincolnshire. Edited by Pat Doody and Brian Barnett. 1987.

No. 8   The moths of Ceredigion. A P Fowles. 1988.

No. 9   Long-term monitoring in unmanaged woodland nature reserves. G F Peterken and Christa Backmeroff. 1988.

No. 10 The woods of Argyll and Bute. Jane MacKintosh. 1988.

No. 11 A woodland survey handbook. K J Kirby. 1988.

No. 12 The reintroduction of the white-tailed sea eagle to Scotland: 1975-1987. Prepared by John A Love. 1988.

No. 13 Saltmarsh vegetation of the Wash. An assessment of change from 1971 to 1985. Margaret I Hill. 1988.

No. 14 The peatland management handbook. T A Rowell. 1988.

No. 15 Woodland conservation and research in the clay vale of Oxfordshire and Buckinghamshire. Proceedings of a symposium . . . on 14 March 1987. Edited by K J Kirby and F J Wright. 1988.

No. 16 NCC research in the uplands. Proceedings of a seminar, 1986. Edited by D B A Thompson, S Whyte and P H Oswald. 1988.

No. 17 The saltmarsh survey of Great Britain. An inventory of British saltmarshes. Fiona Burd. 1989.

No. 18 A sea-cliff bibliography. Compiled by Jonathan Mitchley. 1989.

No. 19 A botanical classification of standing waters in Great Britain and a method for the use of macrophyte flora in assessing changes in water quality. Margaret Palmer. 1989.

No. 20 Vegetated shingle structures survey of Great Britain: Bibliography. Pippa Sneddon and R E Randall. 1989.

No. 21 Dungeness bibliography. Compiled by Helen Riley (assisted by Brian Ferry). 1989.

No. 22 Inventories of ancient, long-established and semi-natural woodland for Scotland. G J Walker and K J Kirby. 1989.

No. 23 The Nature Conservancy Council's research programme (1989/90 edition). Compiled and edited by Philip Oswald and Stefa Birkenhead. 1989.

No. 24 Cut-over lowland raised mires. Proceedings of a conference held on 4 and 5 October 1988 at Doncaster. Edited by Wanda Fojt and Roger Meade. 1989.

No. 25 Moorland management: a literature review. M A Mowforth and C Sydes. 1989.